Cello Exam Pack

ABRSM Initial Grade

Selected from the 2020–2023 syllabus

Contents

Cello consultant: Anita Strevens
Footnotes: Anthony Burton and Kathy Blackwell

Other pieces for Initial Grade
   DUET *with cello accompaniment*   PF/VC *with piano or cello accompaniment*

LIST A

4   **Katherine & Hugh Colledge**   Butterflies: No. 5 from *Waggon Wheels for Cello* (Boosey & Hawkes)

5   **Katherine & Hugh Colledge**   Knickerbocker Glory: No. 11 from *Waggon Wheels for Cello* (Boosey & Hawkes)

6   **Cutter**   Little March, arr. Sassmannshaus (*ending at b. 20*). *Cello Recital Album, Vol. 1* (Bärenreiter) PF/VC

7   **Stanley Fletcher**   Sweet Eyed Sue: No. 9 from *New Tunes for Strings, Cello Book 1* (*with repeat using bowing variation 1*) (Boosey & Hawkes) PF/VC

8   **Sheila Nelson**   Peter Piper (*'E' version*). P. 14 from *Tetratunes for Cello* (Boosey & Hawkes) PF/VC

9   **Trad.**   Big Ben, arr. Passchier, Hussey & Sebba (*upper part*). *Abracadabra Cello (Third Edition)* (Collins Music) PF/VC

10   **Trad.**   Go Tell Aunt Rhody, arr. Suzuki & Mooney. *Suzuki Cello School, Vol. 1* (Alfred) PF/VC

LIST B

4   **Alan Bullard**   Far Away: from *Party Time! for Cello* (*slurs optional*) (ABRSM)

5   **Mary Cohen**   Mrs Andantino Goes for a Walk: from *Superduets for Cello, Book 2* (*upper part*) (Faber) DUET

6   **Thomas Gregory**   Footprints in the Snow. *Vamoosh Cello, Book 1* (Vamoosh)

7   **Edward Huws Jones**   Gone for Good: No. 12 from *Ten O'Clock Rock for Cello* (Boosey & Hawkes)

8   **Sheila Nelson**   Over the Moon. *Piece by Piece 1 for Cello* (Boosey & Hawkes)

9   **Sheila Nelson**   Swingalong (*'E' version*). P. 16 from *Tetratunes for Cello* (Boosey & Hawkes) PF/VC

10   **Trad. French**   French Folk Song, arr. Suzuki & Mooney. *Suzuki Cello School, Vol. 1* (Alfred) PF/VC

LIST C

4   **Kathy & David Blackwell**   Off to School. *Cello Time Starters* (OUP)

5   **Thomas Gregory**   Walk on Mars! (*slides optional; observing DC, as in accomp.*). *Vamoosh Cello, Book 1* (Vamoosh)

6   **Edward Huws Jones**   Ten O'Clock Rock: No. 9 from *Ten O'Clock Rock for Cello* (Boosey & Hawkes)

7   **Caroline Lumsden & Pam Wedgwood**   Jungle Footprints: from *Jackaroo for Cello* (*scream optional*) (Faber)

8   **Sheila Nelson**   Alastair Arbuthnot Has No Hat. *Piece by Piece 1 for Cello* (Boosey & Hawkes)

9   **Trad. German**   Pit a Pat Rain, arr. Sassmannshaus. *Cello Recital Album, Vol. 1* (Bärenreiter) PF/VC

10   **Peter Wilson**   Bow Rock: No. 4 from *Stringpops 1 for Cello* (Faber)

First published in 2019 by ABRSM (Publishing) Ltd,
a wholly owned subsidiary of ABRSM, 4 London Wall Place,
London EC2Y 5AU, United Kingdom
© 2019 by The Associated Board of the Royal Schools of Music
Distributed worldwide by Oxford University Press

Music origination by Julia Bovee
Cover by Kate Benjamin & Andy Potts, with thanks to Brighton College
Printed in England by Halstan & Co. Ltd, Amersham, Bucks.,
on materials from sustainable sources.

Fish Cakes and Apple Pie

Sheila M. Nelson
(born 1936)

This lively piece comes from *Tetratunes*, a book by the composer and string teacher Sheila M. Nelson. All the pieces in this book use four notes on one string and the notes always move up or down by step. The title 'Fish Cakes and Apple Pie' can be sung to the rhythm of the opening bars and this rhythm gives the piece its energetic feeling. All dynamics are editorial suggestions only.

Lightly Row

Arranged by David Blackwell

Trad. German

This piece is a children's song from Germany. It is about a young boy called Hans who leaves home but returns quickly because his mother is unhappy. It is often sung in English to the words, 'Lightly row, lightly row, o'er the shining waves we go', which tells a happier story about sailing on the water.

Polka

Arranged by Sheila M. Nelson

K. A. Wohlfart
(1874–1943)

This bright and cheerful polka, a type of dance originally from central Europe, was written by the Swedish composer and teacher Karl Adrian Wohlfart. As you play it, picture the dancers taking short hopping steps in time to the music.

Waterfall

No. 10 from *Waggon Wheels*

B:1

Katherine Colledge (born 1952)
and Hugh Colledge (born 1945)

Picture a peaceful countryside scene as you play this gentle piece by Katherine and Hugh Colledge. The flowing melody and the piano part with its softly moving quavers suggest that the water is falling gently into a pool at the bottom of a beautiful waterfall. All dynamics are editorial suggestions only.

B:2

All night, all day

Arranged by Nikki Iles

Trad. Spiritual

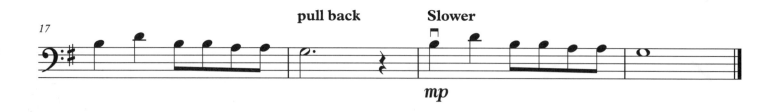

This piece is a spiritual, a type of religious song originally sung in the southern United States. The words of the chorus, 'All night, all day, angels watching over me, my Lord', can be sung to the music in bars 3 to 6.

Silent Friends

Thomas Gregory
(born 1973)

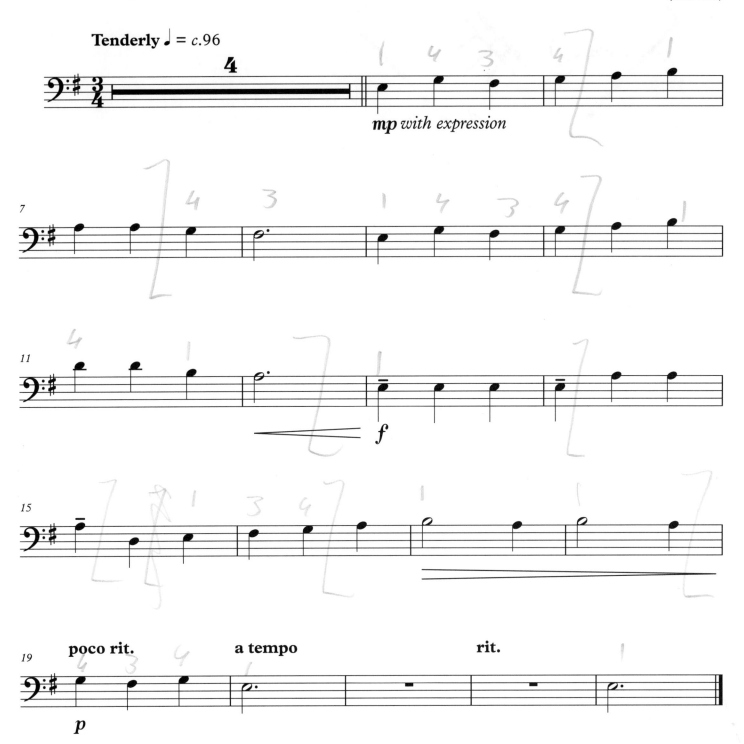

Thomas Gregory is a cellist, conductor and teacher from London. He says that the title *Silent Friends* 'refers to the treasured friendships some share with their pets, toys or even imaginary friends'. This piece, specially written for ABRSM, can be played with other string instruments, as it appears also in the violin, viola and double bass syllabuses. If learning/playing this piece with violins, students may wish to play the Es in bars 13–14 an octave higher (they may be played at either octave in the exam).

On the Prowl

Kathy Blackwell (born 1958)
and David Blackwell (born 1961)

With menace [♩ = *c*.88]

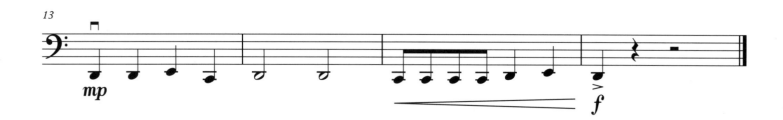

This piece, written by Kathy and David Blackwell, uses a 'rock groove', a strong and repeated rhythm heard here in the piano part that drives the music forward. The composers comment: 'the low notes in both the cello and piano part suggest that something big and heavy is prowling around at night!'

© Oxford University Press 2002
Reproduced by permission from *Cello Time Joggers*. All rights reserved.

Cello Exam Pack

ABRSM Initial Grade

Selected from the 2020–2023 syllabus

Piano accompaniment

Contents

Cello consultant: Anita Strevens
Footnotes: Anthony Burton and Kathy Blackwell

Editorial guidance

We have taken the pieces in this book from a variety of sources. Where appropriate, we have edited the pieces to help you prepare for your performance. We have added metronome markings (in square brackets) and the fingering and bowing indications have been amended where necessary to ensure a consistent approach within the album. Details of other changes or suggestions are given in the footnotes. Fingering, bowing and editorial additions are for guidance only: you do not have to follow them in the exam.

First published in 2019 by ABRSM (Publishing) Ltd,
a wholly owned subsidiary of ABRSM, 4 London Wall Place,
London EC2Y 5AU, United Kingdom
© 2019 by The Associated Board of the Royal Schools of Music
Distributed worldwide by Oxford University Press

Music origination by Julia Bovee
Cover by Kate Benjamin & Andy Potts, with thanks to Brighton College
Printed in England by Halstan & Co. Ltd, Amersham, Bucks.,
on materials from sustainable sources.

Fish Cakes and Apple Pie

Sheila M. Nelson
(born 1936)

This lively piece comes from *Tetratunes*, a book by the composer and string teacher Sheila M. Nelson. All the pieces in this book use four notes on one string and the notes always move up or down by step. The title 'Fish Cakes and Apple Pie' can be sung to the rhythm of the opening bars and this rhythm gives the piece its energetic feeling. All dynamics are editorial suggestions only.

© Copyright 1989 by Boosey & Hawkes Music Publishers Ltd
Reproduced by permission of Boosey & Hawkes Music Publishers Ltd.

Lightly Row

A:2

Arranged by David Blackwell

Trad. German

This piece is a children's song from Germany. It is about a young boy called Hans who leaves home but returns quickly because his mother is unhappy. It is often sung in English to the words, 'Lightly row, lightly row, o'er the shining waves we go', which tells a happier story about sailing on the water.

4

A:3

Polka

Arranged by Sheila M. Nelson

K. A. Wohlfart
(1874–1943)

This bright and cheerful polka, a type of dance originally from central Europe, was written by the Swedish composer and teacher Karl Adrian Wohlfart. As you play it, picture the dancers taking short hopping steps in time to the music.

© Copyright 1992 by Boosey & Hawkes Music Publishers Ltd
Reproduced by permission of Boosey & Hawkes Music Publishers Ltd.

Waterfall

No. 10 from *Waggon Wheels*

B:1

Katherine Colledge (born 1952)
and Hugh Colledge (born 1945)

Picture a peaceful countryside scene as you play this gentle piece by Katherine and Hugh Colledge. The flowing melody and the piano part with its softly moving quavers suggest that the water is falling gently into a pool at the bottom of a beautiful waterfall. All dynamics are editorial suggestions only.

All night, all day

B:2

Arranged by Nikki Iles

Trad. Spiritual

This piece is a spiritual, a type of religious song originally sung in the southern United States. The words of the chorus, 'All night, all day, angels watching over me, my Lord', can be sung to the music in bars 3 to 6.

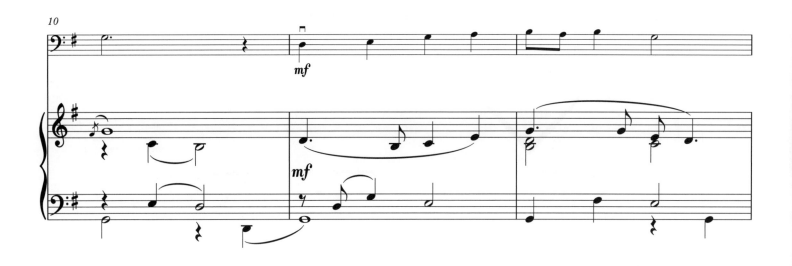

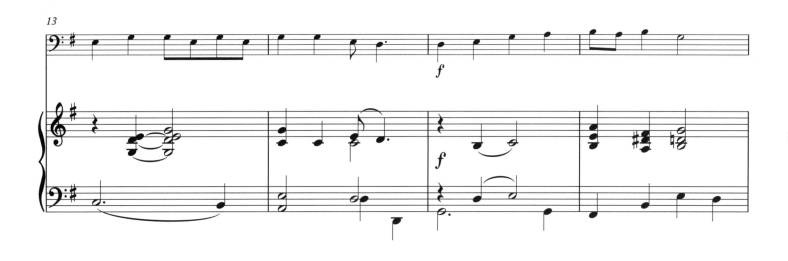

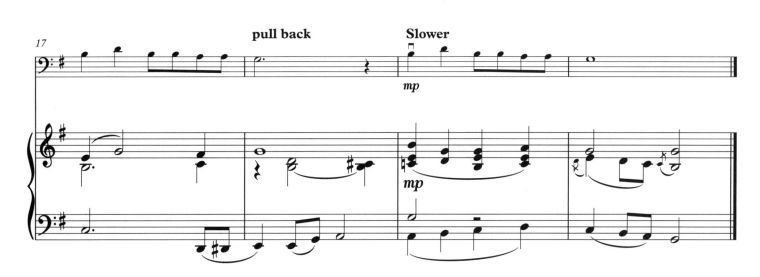

Silent Friends

B:3

Thomas Gregory
(born 1973)

Tenderly ♩ = *c*.96

Thomas Gregory is a cellist, conductor and teacher from London. He says that the title *Silent Friends* 'refers to the treasured friendships some share with their pets, toys or even imaginary friends'. This piece, specially written for ABRSM, can be played with other string instruments, as it appears also in the violin, viola and double bass syllabuses. If learning/playing this piece with violins, students may wish to play the Es in bars 13–14 an octave higher (they may be played at either octave in the exam).

On the Prowl

C:1

Kathy Blackwell (born 1958)
and David Blackwell (born 1961)

With menace [♩ = c.88]

This piece, written by Kathy and David Blackwell, uses a 'rock groove', a strong and repeated rhythm heard here in the piano part that drives the music forward. The composers comment: 'the low notes in both the cello and piano part suggest that something big and heavy is prowling around at night!'

Rock the Boat

from *Party Time!*

Alan Bullard
(born 1947)

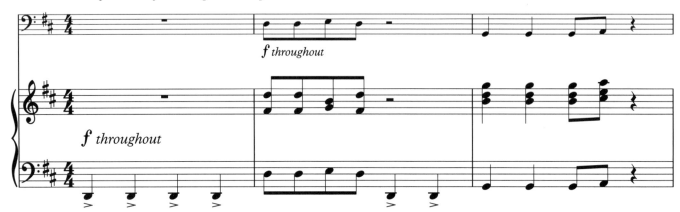

This rhythmic piece was written by the British composer and arranger Alan Bullard. The short notes, strong rhythms, and quick string crossings suggest that this boat is being tossed around from side to side on big waves.

Hill and gully rider

Arranged by Alan Bullard

Trad. Jamaican

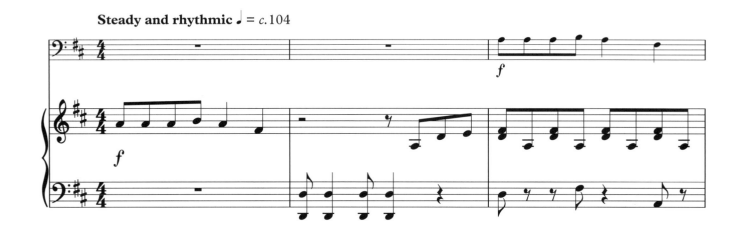

'Hill and gully rider' is a folk song from Jamaica, originally sung by road builders to help them with the hard work of digging ditches (gullies). It is a 'call and response' song in which a leader sings or calls out a line and a group responds with an answering phrase. In this piece each line is answered with the rhythm of the words 'hill and gully' played on the open D string, as in bar 4.

Rock the Boat

from *Party Time!*

C:2

Alan Bullard
(born 1947)

This rhythmic piece was written by the British composer and arranger Alan Bullard. The short notes, strong rhythms, and quick string crossings suggest that this boat is being tossed around from side to side on big waves.

C:3

Hill and gully rider

Arranged by Alan Bullard

Trad. Jamaican

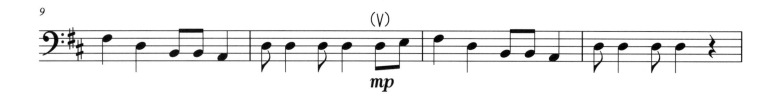

'Hill and gully rider' is a folk song from Jamaica, originally sung by road builders to help them with the hard work of digging ditches (gullies). It is a 'call and response' song in which a leader sings or calls out a line and a group responds with an answering phrase. In this piece each line is answered with the rhythm of the words 'hill and gully' played on the open D string, as in bar 4.

Scales

MAJOR SCALES

from memory
separate bows
even notes *or* long tonic, at candidate's choice

EVEN NOTES

G major — one octave ♪ = 76

D major

LONG TONIC

G major — one octave ♪ = 76

D major

Scales

MINOR SCALE

from memory
separate bows
even notes

A minor

to a fifth ♪ = 76

Sight-reading

Sight-reading